HEART WISE

by Daphne Greaves
illustrated by Marcelo Elizalde

Harcourt
SCHOOL PUBLISHERS

Printed in China

ISBN 10: 0-15-350507-9
ISBN 13: 978-0-15-350507-2

Ordering Options
ISBN 10: 0-15-350333-5 (Grade 3 Below-Level Collection)
ISBN 13: 978-0-15-350333-7 (Grade 3 Below-Level Collection)
ISBN 10: 0-15-357495-X (package of 5)
ISBN 13: 978-0-15-357495-5 (package of 5)

3 4 5 6 7 8 9 10 985 12 11 10 09 08

Characters

Narrator 1   **Matthew**   **Tasha**   **Dr. Stein**

Narrator 2   **Dr. Chico**   **Megan**

Setting: The human heart

Narrator 1: The heart is a symbol of love. On Valentine's Day, people give picturesque cards to loved ones.

Narrator 2: Scientists observe the heart. It is an organ in the human body.

Narrator 1: It is the year 3008. Scientists have a new way to confirm how the heart works.

3

Narrator 2: Submarines travel below the surface of water. Now tiny submarines can travel through the body.

Narrator 1: Scientists have also found a way to shrink people.

Narrator 2: Team Valentine is a group of scientists and students.

Narrator 1: The team's mission is to travel through the heart.

4

Narrator 2: Matthew is a student member. He's keeping a log. Let's take a look.

Matthew: *Day One: Tasha, Megan, and I are lucky to be on this mission. Today we met the scientists.*

Dr. Chico: Who knows what the heart is?

Tasha: It's a muscle.

Megan: It pumps blood through our bodies.

Dr. Stein: Why does blood need to go through the body?

Tasha: Because the blood gives our cells what the body needs.

Dr. Chico: That's right. Blood feeds and fixes the cells.

Dr. Stein: I see we have an excellent team here today.

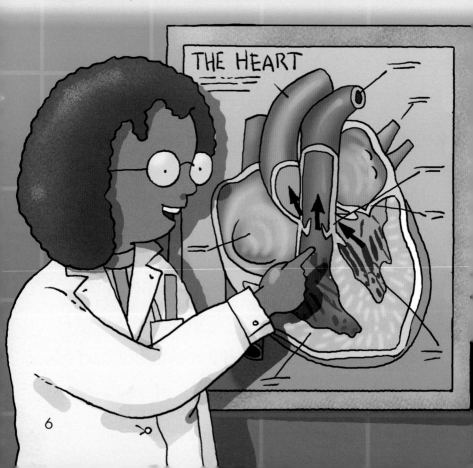

THE HEART

Matthew: *Day Two: Today the team was put into a human body. We hope this mission generates new information about the heart.*

Tasha: We're traveling through the bloodstream! This is incredible!

Dr. Chico: Usually, scientists magnify the blood to study it. Today we've shrunk ourselves. We will take a close up look.

Dr. Stein: Blood cells are one part of the blood.

Dr. Chico: Red blood cells carry oxygen to the body's cells.

Dr. Stein: White blood cells keep the body safe so that bacteria won't erupt into disease. White blood cells treat harmful bacteria.

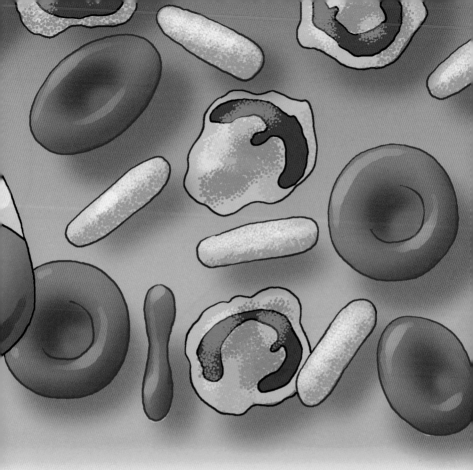

Tasha: What are those tiny grainy things in the blood?

Dr. Chico: They're platelets. They help you stop bleeding when you have a cut.

Megan: Listen! I hear a steady beating.

Dr. Stein: We're getting closer!

Matthew: *Day Three: Today we entered the heart!*

Dr. Chico: The heart has four parts. They are called chambers.

Dr. Stein: Two chambers on top fill up with blood returning from the body.

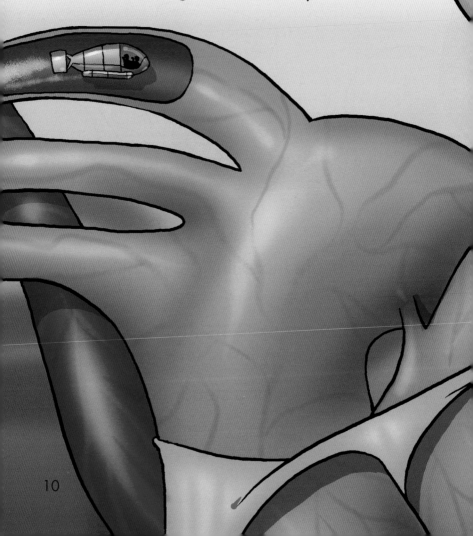

Dr. Stein: Two chambers on the bottom send blood out to the body.

Tasha: This is kind of a bumpy ride!

Megan: I'll say! Now the heart is pushing the blood into a tube.

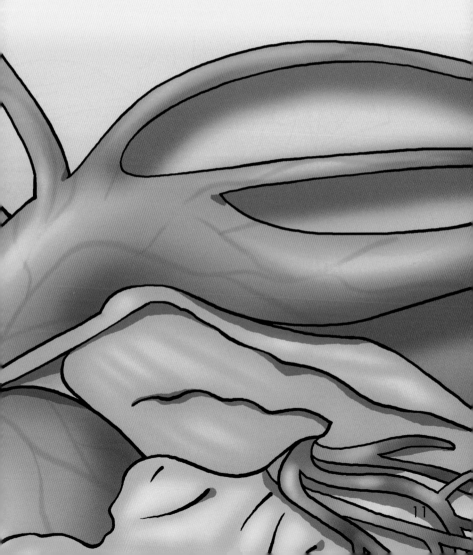

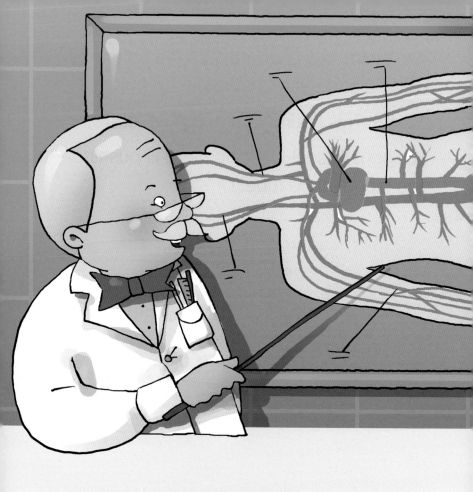

Dr. Chico: That tube is an artery. It is connected to the lungs.

Dr. Stein: First, the blood takes in oxygen in the lungs. Then it takes the oxygen to other body parts. Finally, it travels through the veins and back to the heart again.

Tasha: The blood just keeps spiraling throughout the body?

Dr. Chico: Yes, it circulates throughout the whole body.

Megan: This is so fantastic!

Dr. Chico: The human heart really is an amazing machine.

Dr. Stein: It's time to end our mission.

Matthew: I can't believe we're finished. This has been a great adventure!

Narrator 1: Team Valentine learned many things about the heart. The team worked hard and enjoyed their time together, too.

Narrator 2: Maybe next time they'll visit the brain!

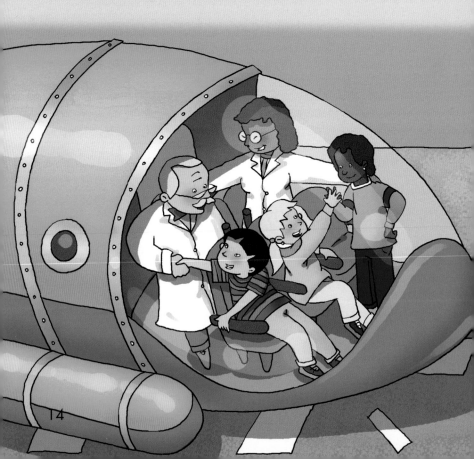

Think Critically

1. Why do you think they called the mission Team Valentine?

2. What did you predict would happen to the team so that they could go on a tiny submarine?

3. What is the setting of this Readers' Theater? How does the setting change?

4. In addition to red and white blood cells, what does the blood contain?

5. Do you think the heart is a good symbol for love? Explain your answer.

 Science

Have a Heart! A good diet is important for a healthy heart. Find out about some foods that are good for the heart and make up a menu for a day that includes these foods.

School-Home Connection Tell family members about this Readers' Theater. Then talk about what you can do to have a healthy heart. Some ideas include exercise and eating healthy foods.

Word Count: 538